DISCARD

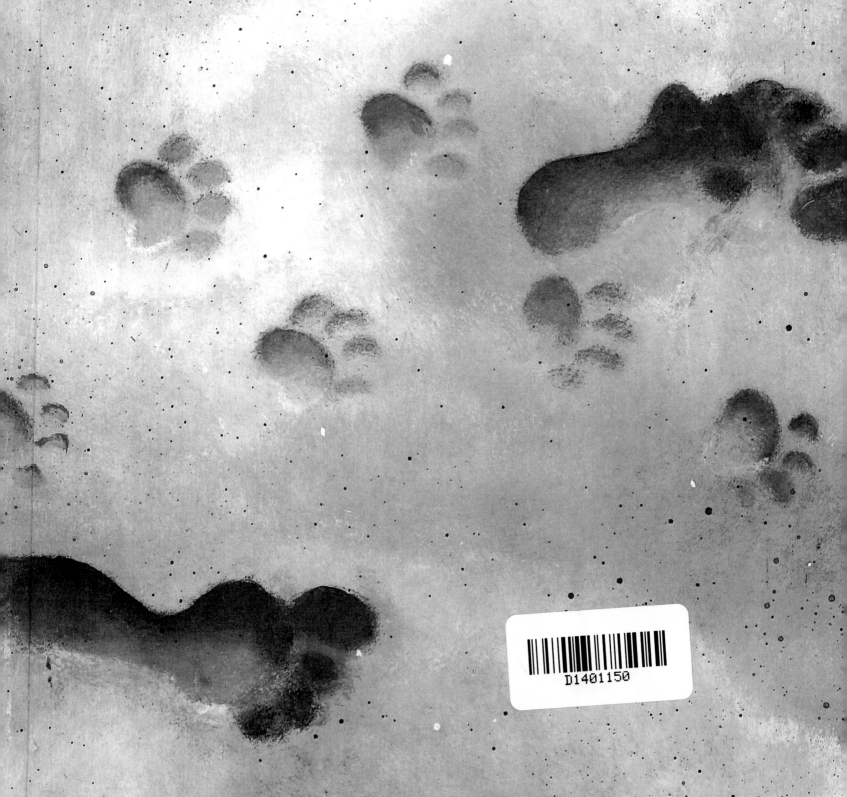

SARAH WALKED TO SCHOOL

Story by

Glenn Shapiro

Illustrations by

Ben Quesnel

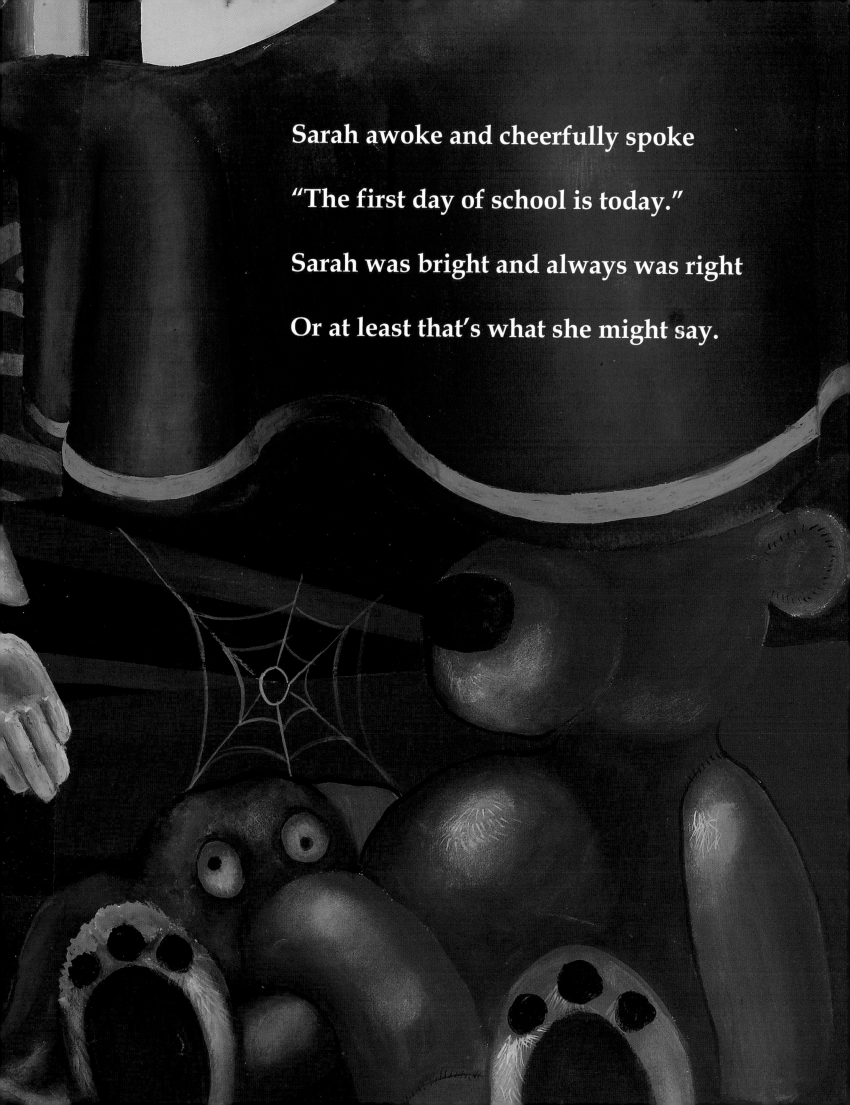

Sarah awoke and cheerfully spoke

"The first day of school is today."

Sarah was bright and always was right

Or at least that's what she might say.

Sarah rushed down to eat and said, from her seat

"I shall walk to school alone today!"

Handing her juice, Mother laughed: "Silly goose.

You don't even know the way."

Sarah's cheeks turned red as she sternly said:

"Now surely you know I'm no fool.

I'll prove that I know just where to go.

Goodbye — I am leaving for school."

Sarah said no more

As she walked out the door

With her head held high in the air.

She looked to the right

And strained her sight

As she said, "I am sure it's down there."

Stomping her feet to the end of the street

She paused, then continued on straight.

"It should be right here, or at least quite near.

Oh, I hope that I won't be too late."

The sun was high

In the brilliant blue sky

When Sarah decided to rest.

"There's no school in sight,

But I know that I'm right.

After all, I always know best."

The sun was going down as Sarah left town

Still certain she knew the right way.

She continued to seek,

Throughout the whole week

Just knowing she'd reach school someday.

It took one month to reach

The Atlantic coast beach,

Sighing, "I'll get there sooner or later.

It won't be too long,

For I'm never wrong."

And she climbed aboard a freighter.

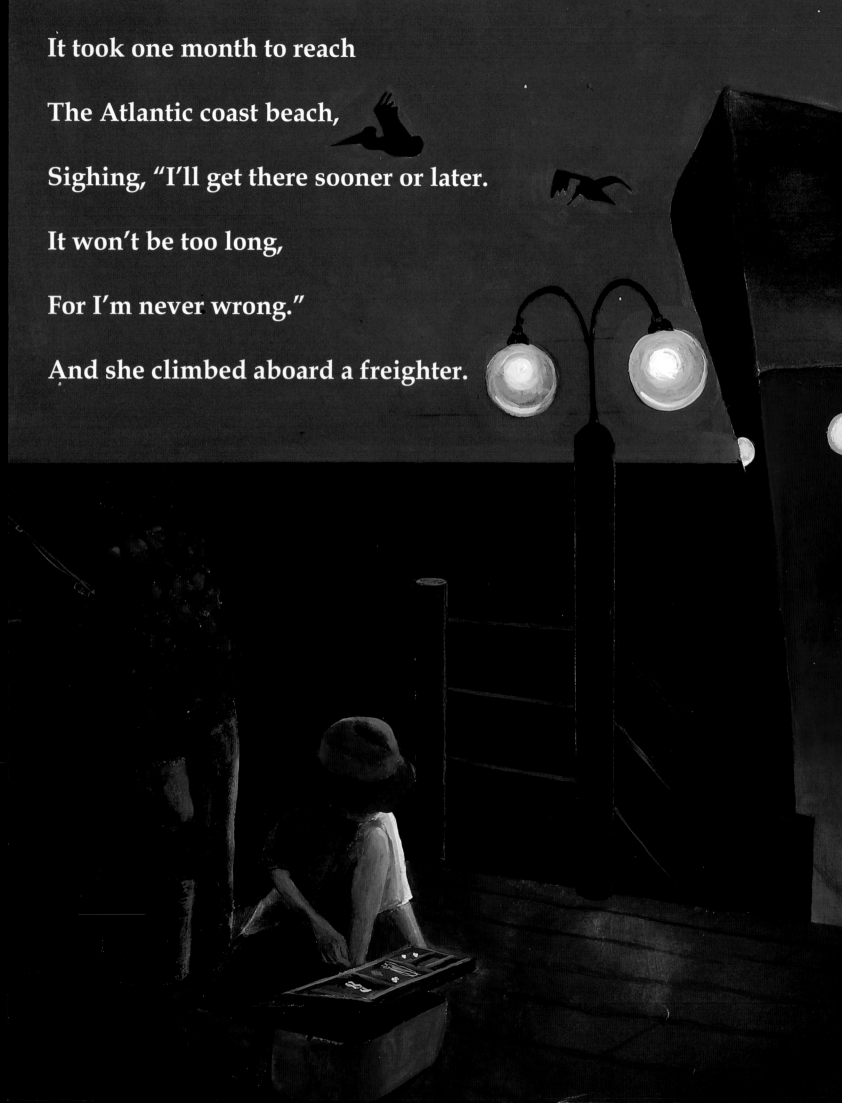

It came as a shock when the boat came to dock

On a strange and distant shore.

It so happened, by chance,

That she had landed in France.

She thought, "I guess I'll just walk some more."

Sarah wandered vast Siberia and trekked across Liberia.

Her determination would not fade.

She held to the notion as she reached the next ocean:

That she soon would start second grade.

Taking ships and a plane

And then boarding a train

A thought came to her that had not before:

"It's taken so long —

Could I have been wrong?

Was the school towards the *left* out my door?"

But then up ahead,

With bricks of bright red

Was a schoolhouse with children at play.

She exclaimed, "What a sight —

I just knew I was right.

I *told* Mother I knew the way."

But Sarah was tall while the kids looked so small.

"The wrong school?" Sarah sighed through her tears.

Then she saw mother's face, and heard her say, "it's the place.

It's just that you've missed a few years!"